For all portable keyboards *by Kenneth Baker*

THE COMPLETE
ROCK & POP
KEYBOARD PLAYER
BOOK 3

Wise Publications
London/New York/Sydney/Cologne

Exclusive Distributors:

Music Sales Limited
8/9 Frith Street, London W1V 5TZ, England.

Music Sales Pty. Limited
27 Clarendon Street, Artarmon, Sydney, NSW 2064, Australia.

This book © Copyright 1986 by Wise Publications.
ISBN 0.7119.0886.9
Order No. AM 62704

Art Direction by Mike Bell.
Designed by Bamber Forsyth Design.
Cover design by Pearce Marchbank.
Arranged by Kenneth Baker.

Music Sales complete catalogue lists thousands of
titles and is free from your local music book shop, or direct
from Music Sales Limited.
Please send 50p in stamps for postage to
Music Sales Limited, 8/9 Frith Street, London W1V 5TZ.

Printed in England by
J.B. Offset Printers (Marks Tey) Limited, Marks Tey.

ABOUT THESE BOOKS

The Complete Rock & Pop Keyboard Player is for all student keyboard players who like good pop music.

The Course features eighteen top groups and solo artists (six in each book). Three songs have been chosen for each artist: there are famous hit songs, songs that are particularly representative of the artist, or simply songs that come off well on an electronic keyboard.

Book One of the Course continues on from Books 1, 2 and 3 of 'The Complete Keyboard Player' (the standard books). In these books you learnt how to use the modern portable electronic keyboard, and how to read music. Using popular standard tunes you learnt basic keyboard techniques, including how to finger correctly, how to play left hand chords, how to play rhythmically.

YOU MUST MASTER THESE EARLY STEPS BEFORE BEGINNING BOOK ONE OF THE PRESENT COURSE.

Whilst the Course is meant to be progressive as it stands, feel free to jump ahead sometimes, or to leave out certain songs, if it suits your particular needs.

Although I have tried to match each written song with the original recording as far as practicable, I found it necessary sometimes to shorten the originals, in order to save awkward page turns. I have also simplified the phrasing of the melodies at times, in order to make reading easier for you. Play along with the original recording if you can, to get the true feeling of the song. I have written mostly in the same key as the record. Where the keys are not the same, use the 'transposer' on your keyboard to compensate.

Look out for the 'double-tracking' songs (there are three or four in each book). You will learn a lot by playing with a pre-recorded track. It will teach you counting and timing as nothing else will, but you may have to persevere to get it right. If you find when laying down your first track that you run out of recording 'space' on your keyboard, leave out a repeat or two.

Whatever you do, have fun!

Billy Joel

Tina Turner

Elton John

Nik Kershaw

Sting

Thompson Twins

CONTENTS

BETTER BE GOOD TO ME

Words & Music by Mike Chapman, Nicky Chinn & Holly Knight

Suggested registration: jazz organ + rock guitar
+ half sustain + chorus (chorale)
Rhythm: rock
Tempo: medium (♩ = 120)

VERSE 1

A pris-'ner of your love. En-tan-gled in your

web. Hot whis - pers in the night. __

I'm cap-tured by your spell.

VERSE 2

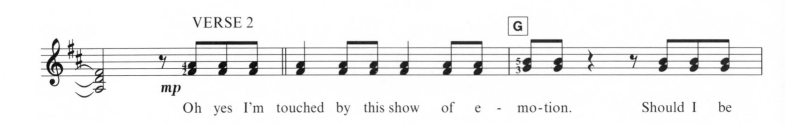

Oh yes I'm touched by this show of e - mo-tion. Should I be

frac-tured by your lack of de - vo-tion? Should I?

Should I?   Oh!   You bet-ter be good to

me.   That's how it's got to   be now.

'Cause I don't have no   use for what you loose-ly call the truth, oh, you bet-ter be good to

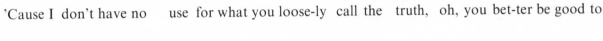

me.   You bet-ter be good. _____

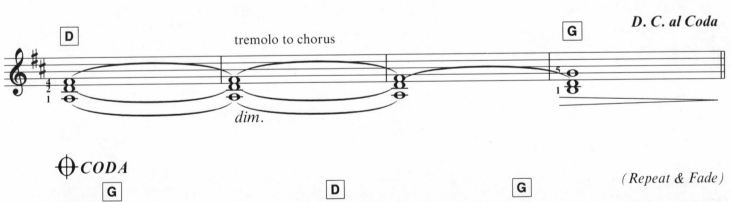

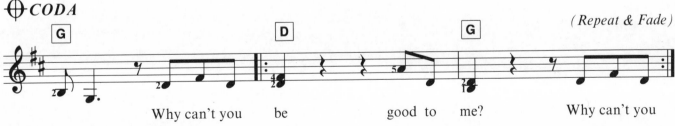

Why can't you   be   good to me?   Why can't you

PRIVATE DANCER

Words & Music by Mark Knopfler

Suggested registration: *jazz organ, with half sustain + trumpet. Chorus (chorale) on.*
Rhythm: rock
Tempo: medium (♩ = 108)

VERSES

Well, the men come in these plac - es, _____
You don't think of them as hum - an, _____

and the men are all the same. _
you don't think of them at all. _____

You don't look at their
You keep your mind on the

fac - es, _____ and you don't ask their name. _
mon - ey, _____ Keep-ing your eyes

CHORUS

tremolo on

on the wall. _ I'm your pri - vate danc - er, a danc-er for mon-ey, I'll

do what you want me to do. _____ I'm your pri - vate danc - er, a

danc - er for mon - ey, and an - y old mu - sic will do.

an - y old mu - sic will do.

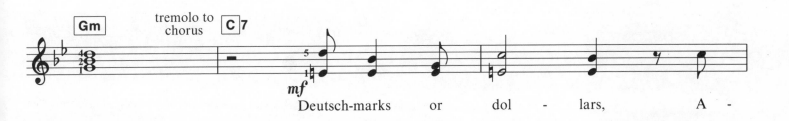

tremolo to chorus

mf

Deutsch-marks or dol - lars, A -

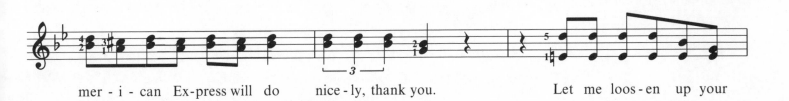

mer - i - can Ex-press will do nice - ly, thank you. Let me loos - en up your

D.% *Fade on CHORUS*

cresc. *ff*

col - lar, ___ Tell me, do you want to see me do the shim-my a - gain?

WHAT'S LOVE GOT TO DO WITH IT

Words & Music by Graham Lyle & Terry Britten

Suggested registration: string ensemble + saxophone
Rhythm: rock
Tempo: medium (♩ = 100)
synchro-start, if available

VERSES

mf

You must un-der-stand that the touch of your hand makes my
may seem to you that I'm act - ing con-fused, when you're

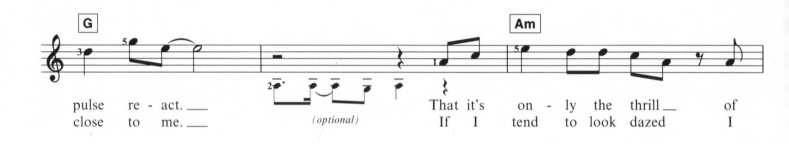

pulse re - act. ___ *(optional)* That it's on - ly the thrill ___ of
close to me. ___ If I tend to look dazed I

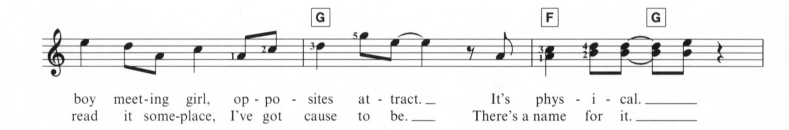

boy meet-ing girl, op-po - sites at - tract. ___ It's phys - i - cal. _____
read it some-place, I've got cause to be. ___ There's a name for it. _____

(optional)

On - ly log - i - cal. _____ You must
There's a phrase that fits. _____ But what -

 CHORUS

f

try to ig - nore that it means more than that. Oh _____ } what's love got to
ev - er the rea - son, you do it for me. Oh _____ }

10

do, got to do with it? What's love but a sec-ond-hand e-mo-tion? __

What's love got to do, got to do with it? Who needs a heart when a

heart can be bro-ken? It heart can be bro-ken? __ I've been tak-ing on a

new di-rec-tion. But I have to say. _____

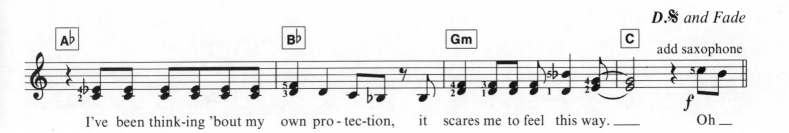

I've been think-ing 'bout my own pro-tec-tion, it scares me to feel this way. ___ Oh __

I WON'T LET THE SUN GO DOWN ON ME

Words & Music by Nik Kershaw

Suggested registration: organ + trombone
+ chorus (chorale)
Rhythm: rock
Tempo: medium (♩ = 108)

VERSES

mp

For - ty   winks in   the   lob - by,   make mine   a   G. and   T.
Moth - er   na - ture isn't in   it,   three hun - dred mil - lion years,

Then to   our fav-'rite hob-by, search-ing for an en - e - my.   Here in   our pa - per hou-ses,
good-bye   in just a min-ute, gone for - ev - er, no more tears.   Pin-ball man, pow-er, glutton,

stretch-ing   for miles and miles,   old men   in strip-ey trou-sers,   rule the world with plas - tic smiles.
vac - uum   in - side his head,   fore-fin - ger on the but-ton,   is he blue or is he red?

F

Good   or ____ bad   like
Break   your __ si - lence

tremolo on

B♭

mf

it   or ____ not.   It's   the ___ on - ly   world we've got. } I
if   you __would be - fore   the ___ sun goes   down for good. }

won't let the sun go down on me, I won't let the sun go

down. I won't let the sun go down on me, I

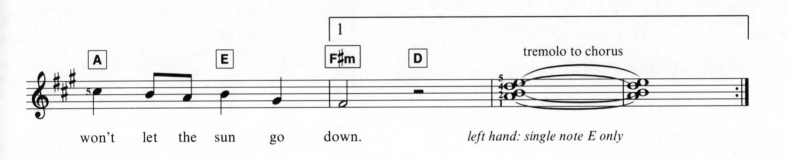

won't let the sun go down. *left hand: single note E only*

tremolo to chorus

down. I won't let the sun go ____ down on me, I

tremolo to chorus

D.% *and Fade*

tremolo on

won't let the sun go ____ down. ____

CHORD OF G♭ (F♯)

1 Using single-finger chord method:

Play G♭ (the lower one of two) in the accompaniment section of your keyboard.

Using fingered chord method:

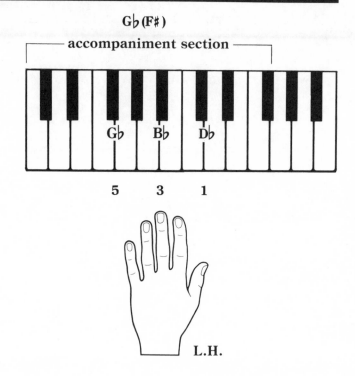

G♭ (F♯)

accompaniment section

G♭   B♭   D♭

5   3   1

L.H.

HUMAN RACING

Words & Music by Nik Kershaw

Suggested registration: brass ensemble + rock guitar + half sustain + chorus
Rhythm: rock
Tempo: medium (♩ = 100)

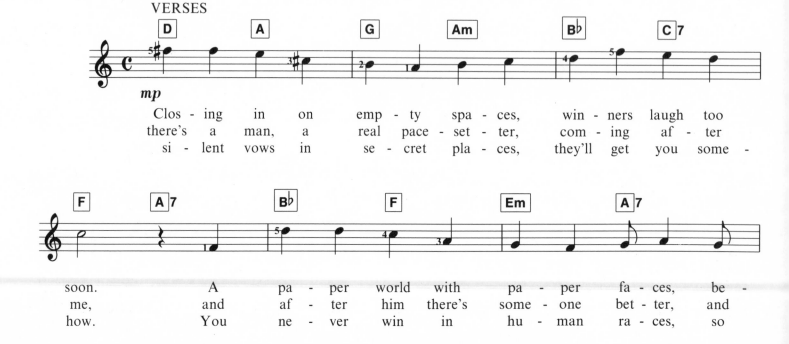

VERSES

| D | A | G | Am | B♭ | C 7 |

mp

Clos - ing   in   on   emp - ty   spa - ces,   win - ners laugh too
there's   a   man,   a   real   pace - set - ter,   com - ing   af - ter
si - lent   vows   in   se - cret   pla - ces,   they'll get   you   some -

| F | A 7 | B♭ | F | Em | A 7 |

soon.   A   pa - per   world   with   pa - per   fa - ces,   be -
me,   and   af - ter   him   there's   some - one   bet - ter,   and
how.   You   ne - ver   win   in   hu - man   ra - ces,   so

neath a pa - per moon. Well, me.
af - ter him there's now
who's the los - er

So

CHORUS

look be - hind ___ you, there's the man ___ you're chas - ing.

Look be - hind ___ you, let's go hu - man rac - ing, hu - man rac -

add rock guitar

- ing. Oh let's go rac - ing now.

CHORD OF C# MINOR (C#m)

2

Using single-finger chord method:

Locate 'C#' (the higher one) in the accompaniment section of your keyboard. Convert this note into 'C#m' (see Book Two, p. 28, and your owner's manual).

Using fingered chord method:

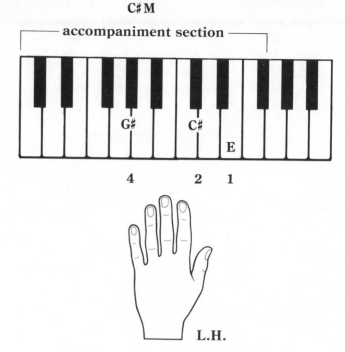

WOULDN'T IT BE GOOD

Words & Music by Nik Kershaw

Suggested registration: harpsichord + rock guitar + half sustain + chorus (chorale)
Rhythm: rock
Tempo: medium (♩ = 104)

VERSES

Bm

mp

I got it bad,   you don't know how bad ___ I got it.
You must be jok—ing,   you don't know a thing ___ a-bout it.

You got it ea-sy,   you don't know when you got it good.   It's get-ting hard-er,   just
You've got no prob-lems,   I'd stay right there, if I were you.   I got it hard-er,   you

C   G

keep-ing life and soul to-geth-er   I'm sick of fight-ing,   ev-en though I know I should.
could-n't dream how hard I got it.   Stay out of my shoes,   if you know what's good for you.

The cold is bit-ing, through each and ev-'ry nerve and fi-bre, my bro-ken spi-rit is
The heat is stif-ling, burn-ing me up from the in-side. The sweat is com-ing through

CHORUS

fro-zen to the core. I don't want to be here no more.
each and ev-'ry pore. Would-n't it be

good to be in your shoes, ev-en if it was for just one day. Would-n't it be

good if we could wish our-selves a-way. Would-n't it be good to be on

your side, the grass is al-ways green-er ov-er there. Would-n't it be good if we could

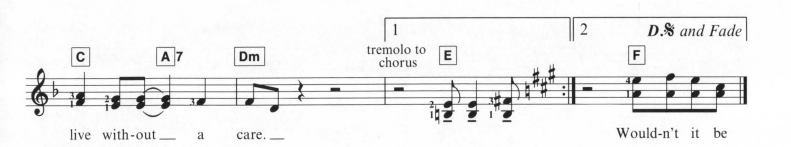

1
tremolo to chorus

2
D.S and Fade

live with-out a care. Would-n't it be

YOUR SONG

Words & Music by Elton John & Bernie Taupin

Suggested registration: string ensemble
Rhythm: rock
Tempo: medium (♩ = 126)

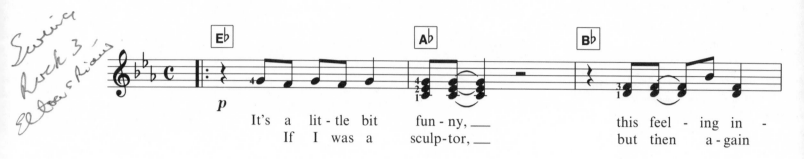

It's a lit - tle bit fun - ny, ___ this feel - ing in -
If I was a sculp-tor, ___ but then a - gain

side. _____ I'm not one of those _____ who can
no, or a man who makes po _____ tions in a

cresc.

eas - i - ly, hide. _____ Don't have much
trav - el - lin' show, _____ I know it's not

mon - ey, _____ but boy, if I did, _____
much, but it's the best I can do, _____

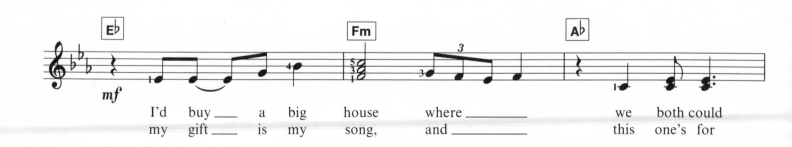

mf

I'd buy ___ a big house where _____ we both could
my gift ___ is my song, and _____ this one's for

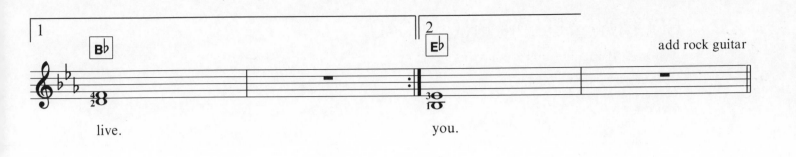

1 **B♭** | 2 **E♭** add rock guitar

live. you.

B♭ | **Cm** | **Fm** | *3*

mp
And you ___ can tell ev - 'ry - bo _____ dy this is your

A♭ *3* | **B♭** | **Cm** | **Fm** | *3*

song. _____ It may be quite __ sim-ple, but now that it's

A♭ *3* | **Cm** | **E♭** | **F 7**

cresc.
done, _____ I hope you don't mind, I hope you don't mind, that I put down in

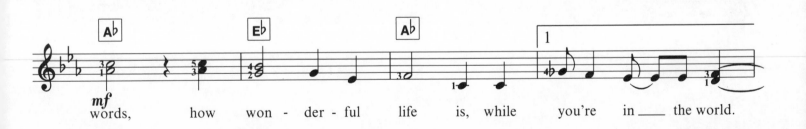

A♭ | **E♭** | **A♭** | 1

mf
words, how won - der - ful life is, while you're in ___ the world.

(D. C.) 2 | **E♭**
cut rock guitar
B♭

___ you're in ___ the world. _____

stop rhythm

GOODBYE YELLOW BRICK ROAD

Words & Music by Elton John & Bernie Taupin

Suggested registration: string ensemble
Rhythm: rock *(as simple as possible)*
Tempo: medium (♩ = 120)

VERSES

mp

When are you gon - na come down,   when are you going to land?   I
What do you think you'll do then?   I bet that-'ll shoot down your plane.   It'll

should have stayed on the farm, ___ should have list-ened to my old man. ___   You
take you a cou - ple of vod - ka and ton - ics to set you on your feet a - gain. ___

know you can't hold me for - ev - er, ___   I did-n't sign up ___ with you.   I'm
May - be you'll get ___ a re - p' -ment, ___ there's plen-ty like me to be found.

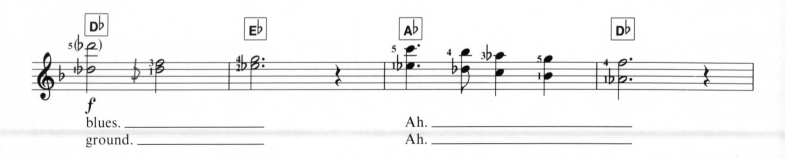

not a pre - sent for your friends to o - pen, this boy's too young to be sing - ing the
Mon-grels who ain't got a pen - ny, sing - ing for tit-bits like you. On the

f

blues. _____   Ah. _____
ground. _____   Ah. _____

DANIEL

Words & Music by Elton John & Bernie Taupin

Suggested registration: brass ensemble, with sustain
Music Programmer: orchestra & chord only (solo off)
Record Backing Track & Chords first.
Rhythm: rock
Tempo: medium (♩ = 120)

Dan - iel is trav - 'ling to - night on a plane.
They say Spain is pret - ty, though I've nev-er been.

I can see the red tail lights head-ing for Spa in.
Well Dan - iel says it's the best place he's ev er seen.

Oh and I can see Dan - iel wav-ing good-bye.
Oh and he should know he's been there e - nough.

God, it looks like Dan-iel,
Lord, I miss Dan-iel,

CHORUS

KING OF PAIN

Words & Music by Sting

Suggested registration: string ensemble
+ synthe
Rhythm: rock
Tempo: medium (♩ = 120)

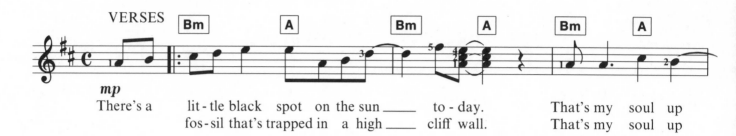

VERSES | Bm | A | Bm | A | Bm | A

mp

There's a   lit-tle black   spot   on the sun _____ to - day.   That's my   soul   up
fos-sil that's trapped in   a   high _____ cliff wall.   That's my   soul   up

Bm | A | G | A | G | A | F#m

there.   It's the   same   old   thing as ___ yes   - ter -day. _   That's my   soul   up
there.   There's a   dead salmon fro - zen in   a   wat-er-fall. _   That's my   soul   up

G | Bm | A | Bm | A | Bm | A

there.   There's a   black hat   caught   in the high _____ tree top.   That's my   soul   up
there.   There's a   blue whale   beached by   a   spring   - tide's ebb.   That's my   soul   up

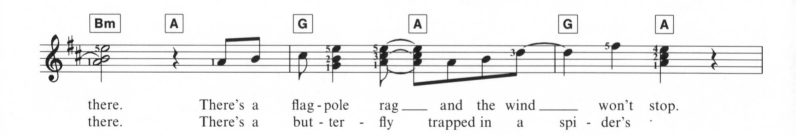

Bm | A | G | A | G | A

there.   There's a   flag - pole   rag ___ and the wind _____ won't   stop.
there.   There's a   but - ter - fly   trapped in   a   spi - der's

CHORUS

F#m | G | 𝄋 A | G

That's my   soul   up   there.   }   I   have   stood here be - fore   in - side the
That's my   soul   up   there.   }   *f*

24

pour - ing rain, with the world turn-ing cir - cles run-ning 'round my brain. I guess

I'm al-ways hop - ing that you'll end this reign, but it's my des - ti - ny to be the

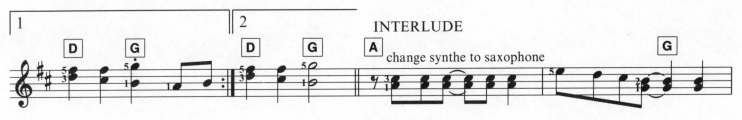

INTERLUDE
change synthe to saxophone

King of pain. There's a King of pain. There's a King on a throne with his eyes torn

out, there's a blind man look-ing for a shad-ow of doubt. There's a rich man sleep-ing on a gold-en

D. $ al Coda
saxophone to synthe

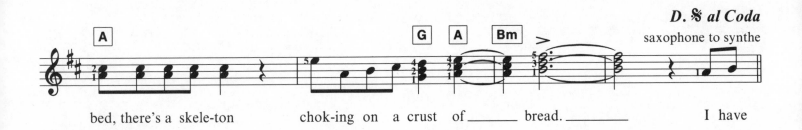

bed, there's a skele-ton chok-ing on a crust of _____ bread. _____ I have

CODA   *(Repeat & Fade)*

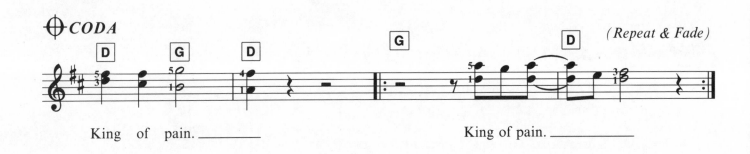

King of pain. _____   King of pain. _____

WRAPPED AROUND YOUR FINGER

Words & Music by Sting

Suggested registration: bright piano, with
medium sustain + chorus (chorale)
Rhythm: rock
Tempo: medium (♩ = 126)

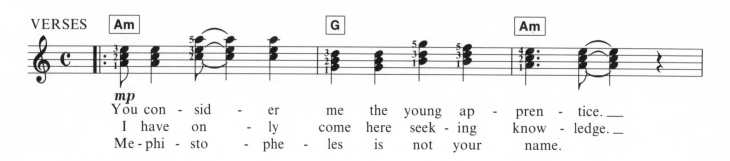

VERSES

You con - sid - er me the young ap - pren - tice. ___
I have on - ly come here seek - ing know - ledge. ___
Me - phi - sto - phe - les is not your name.

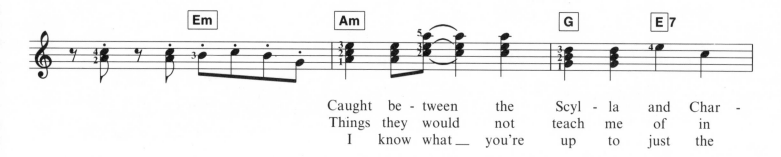

Caught be - tween the Scyl - la and Char -
Things they would not teach me of in
I know what ___ you're up to just the

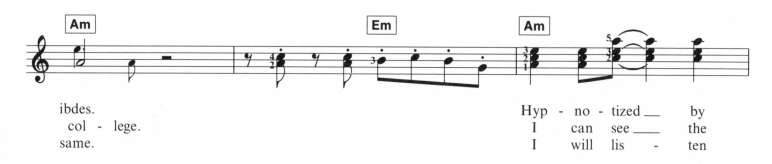

ibdes.
col - lege.
same.

Hyp - no - tized ___ by
I can see ___ the
I will lis - ten

you, if I should lin - ger. ___
des - ti - ny you sold.
hard to your tu - i - tion. ___

add trumpet
2nd & 3rd times

Star - ing at ___ the ring a - round your fin - ger. ___
Turned in - to ___ a shin - ing band of gold.
You will see ___ it come to its fru - i - tion. ___

CHORUS

I'll ___ be   wrapped a - round   your

fin - ger. ___   I'll ___ be ___

wrapped a - round   your   fin - ger. ___

INSTRUMENTAL

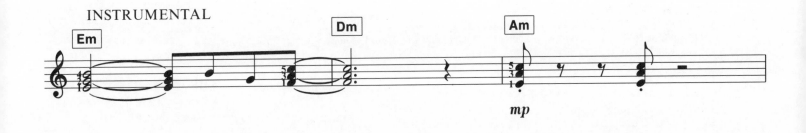

mp

D. C. *(3rd Verse) then*
Repeat CHORUS and Fade

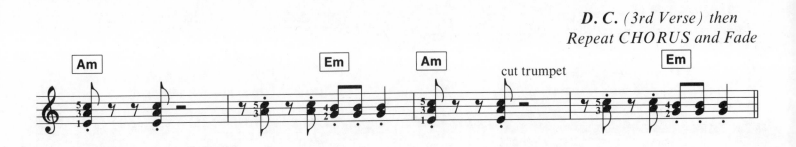

ROCK IN $\frac{6}{4}$ TIME

3 In 'Synchronicity I', a powerful and original rock number recorded by The Police, there are six quarter notes (crotchets) per bar, instead of the usual four (or two). This gives rise to a most interesting and compulsive rhythm. Think of each bar as containing three half notes (minims):

count: 1   2   3

then fit in the intermediate notes accordingly.

As an example, here's how you might count and play BARS 1 and 3 of Synchronicity (typical bars):

THE RHYTHM UNIT IN $\frac{6}{4}$ TIME

4 Since you are unlikely to have a $\frac{6}{4}$ rock rhythm available on your keyboard, you will have to make do in Synchronicity with a normal $\frac{4}{4}$ rock rhythm. Shut your ears to the wrong accents, and just keep going.

SYNCHRONICITY 1

Words & Music by Sting

Suggested registration: jazz flute + chorus (chorale) Arpeggio if available.
Music Programmer: orchestra & chord to record (solo off) Record Melody Track & Chords first.
Rhythm: rock
Tempo: fast (♩ = 200)

28

they know me. __ Ex-tra-sen-so-ry __ syn-chro-ni-ci-ty. __

A star fall, __ a phone call, it joins all, __

CHORUS

syn-chro-ni-ci-ty. __

add synthe
or trumpet

A con-nec-ting prin-ci-ple, linked to the in-vis-i-ble,

al-most im-per-cept-i-ble, some-thing in-ex-press-i-ble. Sci-ence in-sus-cept-i-ble

log-ic so in-flex-i-ble, caus-al-ly con-nect-i-ble, noth-ing is in-vin-ci-ble.

add duet

SISTER OF MERCY

Words & Music by T. Bailey, A. Currie & J. Leeway

Suggested registration: vibraphone,
with slight sustain
Rhythm: reggae (or rock)
Tempo: medium (♩ = 112)
synchro-start, if available

VERSE 1

p

She lives   in a big white house.

The rooms are lem - on and she's de - vot - ed to

life,   of keep-ing this house ___ just

right, ooh. ___ The week-ends are per -fect-ly nice, ooh. ___ She does-n't talk when

VERSES 2 & 3

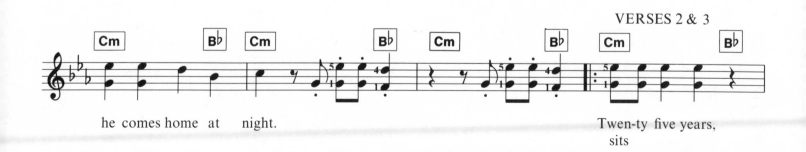

he comes home at night.

Twen-ty five years,
sits

32

she's just the   same.
in a big white   chair.
                              She's a lone - ly wo-man,
                              In a   room that's not so

qui - et   in her   ways.
dif-f'rent to the one back   there.
                              Then   he comes home one
                              She   turns her face to the

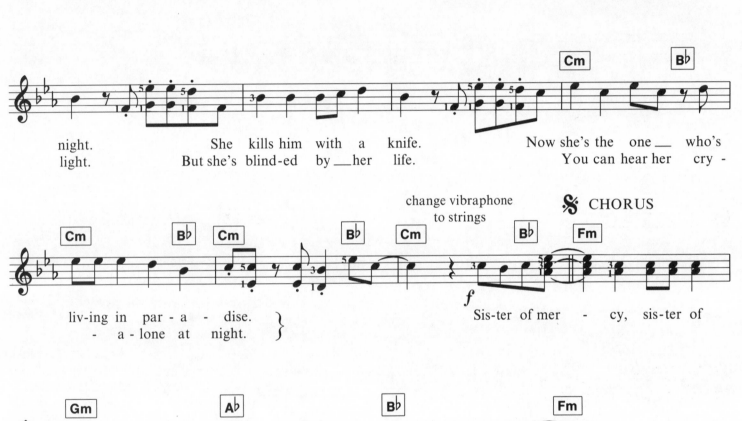

night.
light.
           She kills him with a   knife.
           But she's blind-ed by __her   life.
                              Now she's the one __ who's
                              You can hear her   cry -

change vibraphone
to strings   𝄋 CHORUS

liv-ing in par - a - dise. }
  - a - lone at   night. }
f   Sis-ter of mer - cy, sis-ter of

mer - cy, oh don't ____   cry for __ me.   Sis-ter of mer - cy, __ sis-ter of

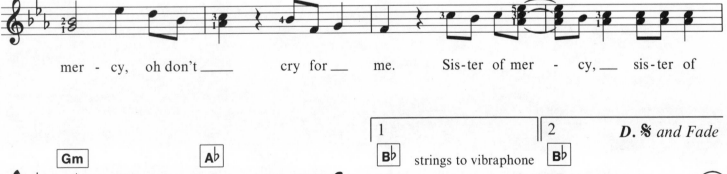

1   **2**   ***D. 𝄋 and Fade***

strings to vibraphone

mer - cy, it's all, ____ al-right by   me.   Now she me.   Sis-ter of mer -
                                   p   *f*

YOU TAKE ME UP

Words & Music by T.Bailey, A.Currie & J.Leeway

Suggested registration: marimba (or vibes),
with half sustain.
Rhythm: reggae (or rock)
Tempo: medium (♩ = 108)
synchro-start, if available

VERSE 1

I work on the front line   I work to sur-vive.   I

sleep in a fe - ver,   so this is my life.   I

cry in my sleep.   Cry boy.__ Cry boy.__ Just makes me weep when I   try how I try.   I

change marimba
to string ensemble

know what it means to work hard on ma-chines, it's a   la-bour of love so please don't ask me why.   I'm

VERSES 2 & 3

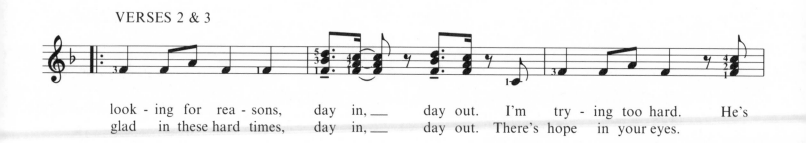

look - ing for rea - sons,   day in, __   day out. I'm   try - ing too hard.   He's
glad   in these hard times,   day in, __   day out. There's hope   in your eyes.

try - ing ___ too hard.   I'm mov - ing in cir - cles,   too hot,   too hot, don't
Hope in ___ his eyes.   I need a re - li - gion,   too hot,   too hot, this

get ver - y far. Don't get ver - y far. Should I   ask you to dance?   Dance boy,   dance boy. I
love nev-er dies.   love nev - er dies. I   be - lieve in to - day, be - lieve boy, be - lieve boy. It's

pro - mise ro-mance will you   come for the ride?   I   know what it means to work
bet - ter that way, and you   work through the night.

§ CHORUS

add arpeggio

hard on ma-chines. Do you   be-lieve in love, one that   lasts for all time? You take me   up,   Oh,
It's a   la-bour of love   so please don't ask me why. You take me

oh,   you take me   up to the high-er ground. ___ You take me   up   so   high. ___   Now I

1.
2.
cut arpeggio
D.§ and Fade

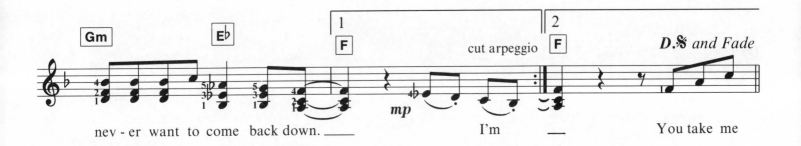

nev - er want to come back down. ___   I'm ___   You take me

THE GAP

Words & Music by T.Bailey, A.Currie & J.Leeway

Suggested registration: clarinet + chorus (chorale)
Rhythm: disco (or rock)
Tempo: medium (♩ = 112)
synchro-start, if available

1. Wake up   in   a strange land,   one   of   for - ty thieves.
2. Beg - gars in   the back-streets,   there for   all   the world to leave.
3. Can you smell the per - fume   of   a   hund - red thou-sand years?

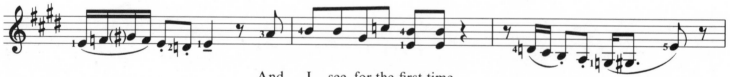

And   I   see for the first time
It's you that's beg-ging for at - ten-tion,
Dare you   look in - to the eyes

Well it's
that hide a

just what you be - lieve.   I   go down to the mar - ket,
all   the same to me.   And   I   won't ask per - mis - sion,
hund-red mill-ion tears,   and there's no   need to   be so fright-ened,

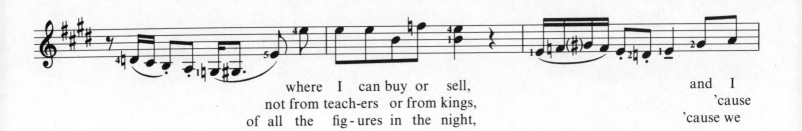

where I can buy or sell,
not from teach-ers or from kings,
of all the fig-ures in the night,

and I
'cause
'cause we

lis-ten to the chant-ing,
I can see for my-self
shared the same e-mo-tions

and all the lies the wise ones tell.
all the pain that you will bring.
and no-one's wrong and no-one's right.

CHORUS

duet on

G **F#**

They say *f* east is east,

west is west,

F **E** **Em**

two dif-f'rent col-ours on the map.
two dif-f'rent rhy-thms to the rap.

We say break the line,

F# **F** **E**

duet off

chew the fat.

Keep mov-ing out in-to the gap.

D. % *(Verse 3) Fade on CHORUS*

change clarinet to string ensemble

strings to clarinet

mf

(play 4 times)

THE ENTERTAINER

Words & Music by Billy Joel

Suggested registration: jazz guitar + synthe
+ chorus (chorale)
Rhythm: rock
Tempo: fast   (♩ = 208)

VERSES

1. I   am   the   en - ter - tain - er,   and I   know   just   where   I
(2) am   the   en - ter - tain - er,   and I've   had   to   pay   my
(3) am   the   en - ter - tain - er,   been   all   a - round   the

stand.   An - oth - er   ser - e - nad - er,   and an - oth - er   long-haired
price.   The things   I   did   not   know at first   I____ learned by   do - ing
world.   I've played all   kinds of   plac - es,   and __ laid all   kinds of

band.   To - day   I   am your   cham - pion,   I   may have won your
twice.   But   still they come to   haunt me.   Still   they want their
girls.   I   can't re - mem - ber   fac - es,   I   don't re - mem - ber

hearts,   but I   know the game, you'll for - get my   name, and   I won't be   here in an -
say.   So I've learned to dance with a   hand in my pants, I let 'em rub my   neck and I
names.   But what the hell, you know it's just as   well, 'cause   af - ter a while, and a

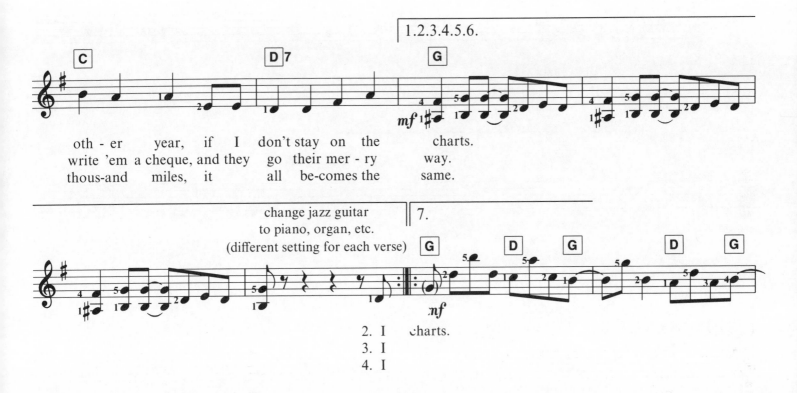

oth - er   year, if I   don't stay on the   charts.
write 'em a cheque, and they   go their mer - ry   way.
thous-and   miles, it   all be-comes the   same.

change jazz guitar
to piano, organ, etc.
(different setting for each verse)

2. I   charts.
3. I
4. I

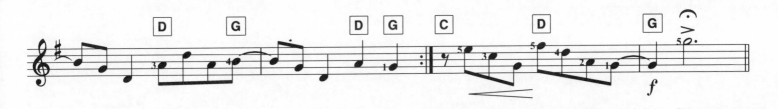

4. I am the entertainer, I bring you my songs,
    I'd like to spend a day or two,
    but I can't stay that long.
    I got to meet expenses,
    I got to stay in line,
    Got to get those fees to the agencies
    And I'd love to stay but there's bills to pay
    So I just don't have the time.

5. I am the entertainer, I've come to do my show,
    You've heard my latest record,
    it's been on the radio.
    It took me years to write it,
    they were the best years of my life,
    If you're gonna have a hit you gotta make it fit
    So they cut it down to 3:05.

6. I am the entertainer, the idol of my age,
    I make all kinds of money
    when I go on the stage.
    You see me in the papers,
    I've been in the magazines,
    But if I go cold, I won't get sold,
    I get put in the back in the discount rack
    Like another can of beans.

7. I am the entertainer and know just where I stand,
    Another serenader and another long - haired band.
    Today I am your champion,
    I may have won your hearts,
    But I know the game, you'll forget my name,
    I won't be here in another year
    If I don't stay on the charts.

STREET LIFE SERENADER

Words & Music by Billy Joel

Suggested registration: *jazz flute.*
Duet + variation: on
Rhythm: 16 beat (rock)
Tempo: slow (♩ = 72)

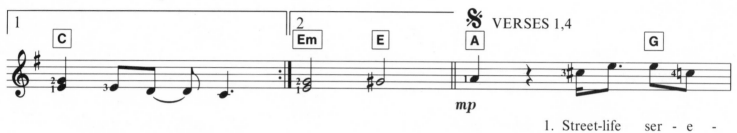

1. Street-life   ser - e -
4. Street-life   ser - e -

nad - er, _____   nev - er sang   on   stag - es. _____
nad - ers, _____   have no ob - li - ga - tions. __

Needs no   or - ches - tra - tion, _____   mel - o - dy comes
Hold no grand il - lu - sions, _____   need no sti - mu -

VERSES 2,3,5

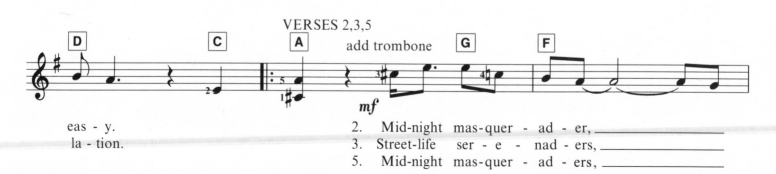

eas - y.
la - tion.

2. Mid-night mas-quer - ad - er, _____
3. Street-life   ser - e - nad - ers, _____
5. Mid-night mas-quer - ad - ers, _____

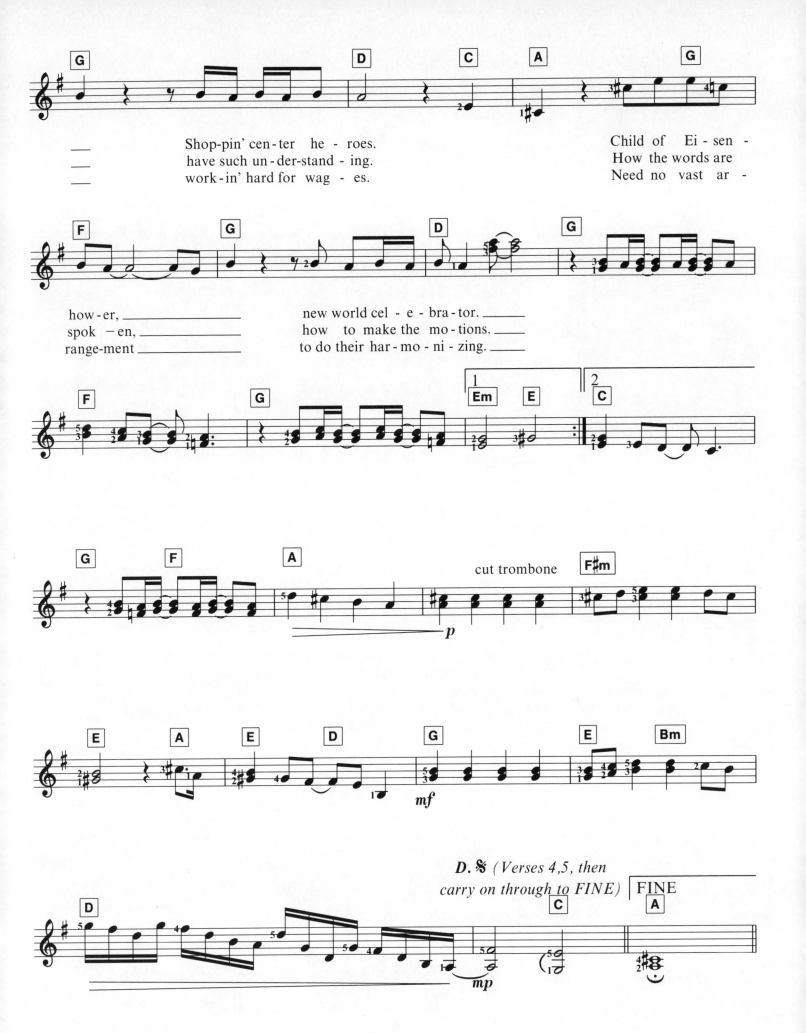

THE BALLAD OF BILLY THE KID

Words & Music by Billy Joel

Suggested registration: piano, with half-sustain
Chorus (chorale) on.
Music Programmer: orchestra & chord only (solo off)
Record Melody Track & Chords first.
Rhythm: 16 beat (or rock, running at double speed)
Tempo: slow, with double time feel (♩ = 88)

CHORD CHART

5

(Showing all 'fingered chords' used in The Complete Rock & Pop Keyboard Player).

C
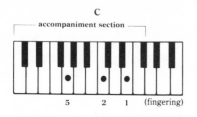

Cm
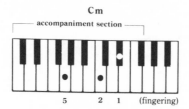

C7
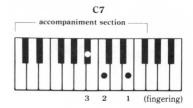

D♭
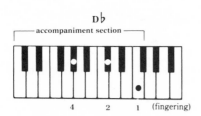

C♯m
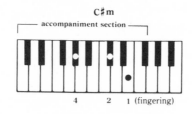

D
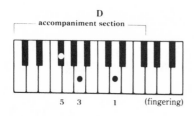

Dm
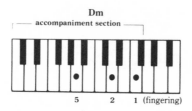

D7
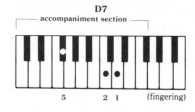

E♭
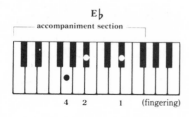

E♭m
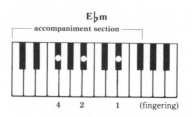

E
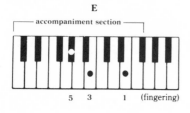

Em
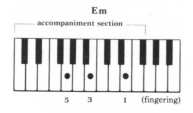

E7
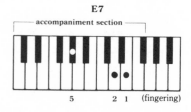

F
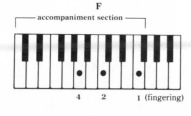

Fm
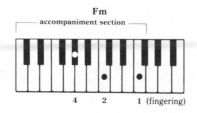

F7
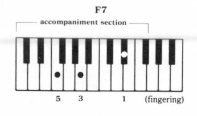

G♭(F♯)

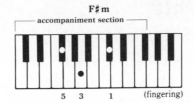

F♯m

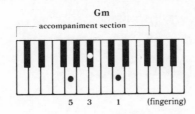

G

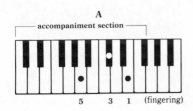

Gm

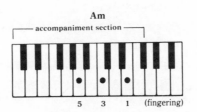

G7

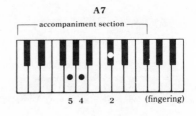

A♭

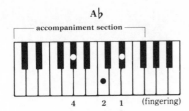

A

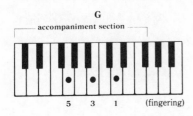

Am

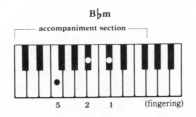

A7

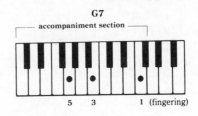

B♭

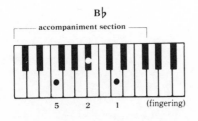

B♭m

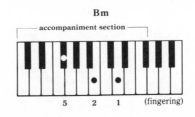

B

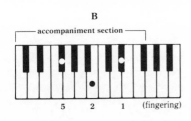

Bm

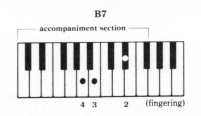

B7

DISCOGRAPHY

ARTIST	TITLE	ALBUM No
Billy Joel	Streetlife Serenade	CBS CBS32035
	Songs In The Attic	CBS CBS32364
Elton John	Goodbye Yellow Brick Road	DJM DJLPD 1001/2
	Elton John	DJM DJLPS 406
	Single Man	Rocket Train 1
Nik Kershaw	Human Racing	MCA MCF 3197
The Police	Synchronicity	A&M AMLY 63735
The Thompson Twins	Into The Gap	Arista 205971
Tina Turner	Private Dancer	Capitol TINA 1